D1198203

35

PIXies

by Jack Wohl

HOLT, RINEHART and WINSTON
New York   Chicago   San Francisco

Copyright © 1966, by United Feature Syndicate, Inc.

First Published in book form in April, 1967.

All rights reserved, including the right to reproduce
this book or portions thereof in any form.

Published simultaneously in Canada by Holt, Rinehart
and Winston of Canada, Limited.

Library of Congress Catalog Card Number: 67-13479

FIRST EDITION

Cover and Book Designed by: Harold Franklin

8640351
Printed in the United States of America

THE ESSENTIAL FACTS

What are PIXies, you ask?
One might as well ask what is Jack Wohl.
A good question. Jack Wohl is, first, a tall person.
He is also a writer, an artist, a husband, a father, and
a friend of other persons, some tall, some short.

And he is the inventor of all the PIXies in this book. Which brings us back to the original question. PIXies are just like people, only different. That is to say, PIXies are happy or sad; angry or gay; frustrated or fulfilled; depending.

But Jack Wohl has found a new means of artistic expression, in which the philosophical truisms of the ages can be summed up in just a handful of symbols.

ABCDefgHijkLMNoPQR
stUvwXyz&'!?$67890

All right. Seven hands full of symbols.

Imagine! Jack Wohl has revolutionized the art of communication. Consider.

What is **E**, if not an **F** who has grown a foot over the summer?

Understand?

To put it another way, **5** is an **S** who's standing at attention. And **B**, an expectant **P**. What is an **O**, if not a **Q** after plastic surgery?

Suddenly it becomes clear. Letters and numbers have

lives of their own. They are big and small. Thick and thin. Straight and curly. They have the power to express the ultimate conflict between good and evil in black and white.

Until PIXies, letters have existed only to serve the nefarious purposes of man. Their own struggles and aspirations have been largely neglected. But in PIXies, they finally find a voice of their own.

A voice at once robust and plaintive, assertive and entreating, romantic and realistic.

And funny. Always funny.

Because Jack Wohl is a **funny** tall person.

Spend some time with his PIXies and you'll agree.

—A short friend

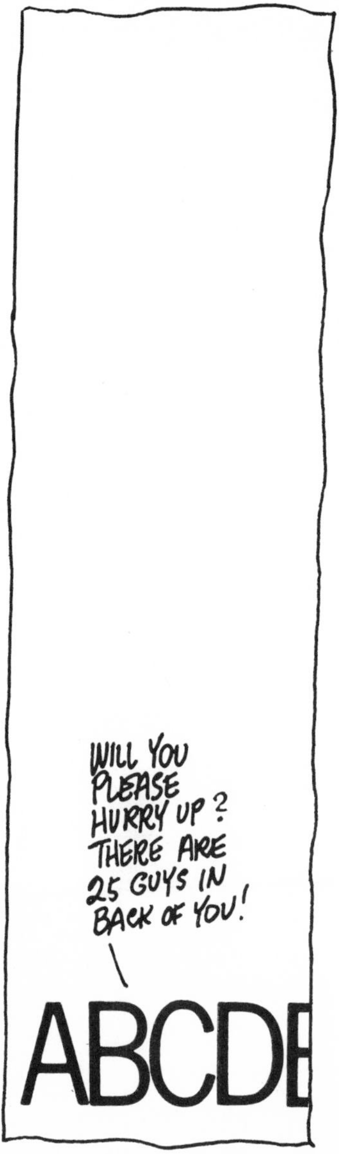
WILL YOU PLEASE HURRY UP? THERE ARE 25 GUYS IN BACK OF YOU!
ABCDE

LOOK, ALVIN... WE BOTH CAN'T BE FIRST!
A 1

GOLLY.. I'VE NEVER SEEN SIAMESE TWINS BEFORE!
n m

I'M SORRY TO TELL YOU THIS, SIR... BUT YOU'VE TAKEN A TURN FOR THE WORSE.

I KNOW, I KNOW... WE WALK TEN PACES AND FIRE.

DON'T DENY IT, FRED. YOU KNOW YOU MARRIED ME FOR MY MONEY.

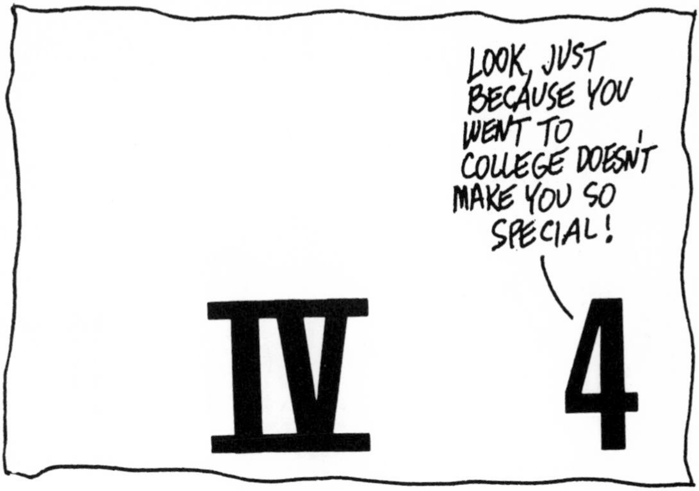
LOOK, JUST BECAUSE YOU WENT TO COLLEGE DOESN'T MAKE YOU SO SPECIAL!
IV
4

SAY.. WHY DON'T WE GET TOGETHER JUST FOR LAUGHS?
h
a

HEY, STUPID, HE SAID RIGHT FACE!!

bbdb

EDDIE, I THINK YOU'RE SLIPPING.

EE

IT'LL NEVER WORK, NORMAN. WE'RE FROM TWO DIFFERENT WORLDS.

N *N*

WITHOUT YOU.. I'M NOTHING.
10

BERNARD... WHEN ARE YOU GOING TO REALIZE THAT NOBODY LIKES A SHOWOFF!
B B

HELLO, GEORGE, WHO'S THE CUTE LITTLE NUMBER?
M M2

HAVE YOU GUYS EVER BEEN IN A THREE-LEGGED RACE BEFORE?

Y'KNOW... I FEEL LIKE A NEW PERSON SINCE I HAD IT REMOVED.

FOR GOODNESS' SAKE, ALBERT.. YOU SURE DANCE CLOSE!

I HOPE I'M NOT BORING YOU GUYS.
ZZZZ2

YOU'RE JUST WHAT I'VE BEEN LOOKING FOR, EDNA. A GOOD OLD-FASHIONED GIRL.
EE

ALBERT, THOSE SHOES DO WONDERS FOR YOU.
AA

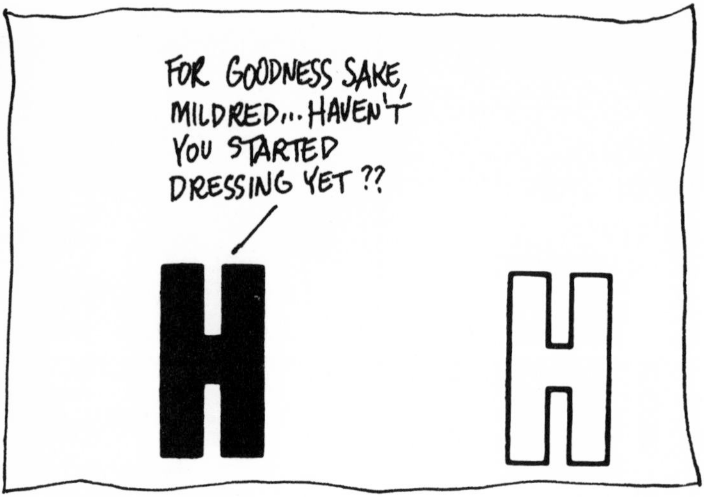
FOR GOODNESS SAKE, MILDRED... HAVEN'T YOU STARTED DRESSING YET ??

SOME GUYS HAVE ALL THE LUCK!
7 13

I'M AFRAID THAT LAST MARTINI WENT TO MY HEAD.
88

WATCH IT...
HERE COMES
TROUBLE.
12 13

WHY DON'T
WE USE A
PLANE LIKE
EVERYBODY
ELSE?
LSD

EDNA,,
YOU'RE ALL
HEART.

ISN'T IT AMAZING WHAT A GOOD GIRDLE CAN DO?
8 00

KICK, STUPID! KICK!!
RRP

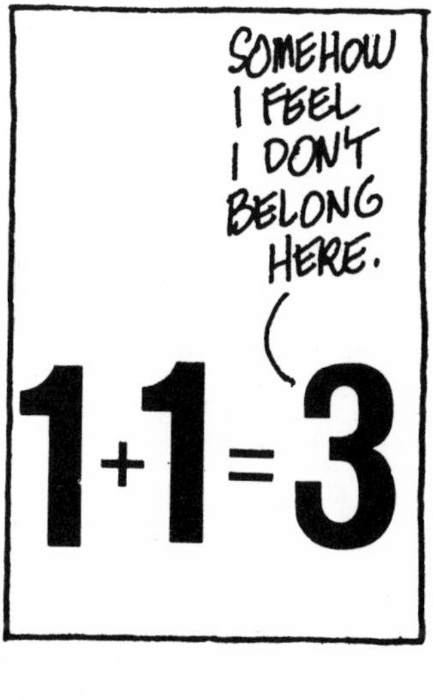
SOMEHOW I FEEL I DON'T BELONG HERE.
1+1=3

THE NICE THING ABOUT YOU AND ME IS.. WE AGREE ON EVERYTHING.
O K
WELL... HOW'S THAT FOR A MARTINI?
H H
THAT'S FUNNY.. YOU DON'T LOOK FIVE.
5 V

WHY IS IT, OLIVIA... YOU'RE THE ONLY GIRL I CAN'T GET STARTED WITH?
N O
IRVING... GET OFF DADDY'S BACK!
n h
DDT
YOU DIRTY, ROTTEN, MURDERERS, YOU!!!

DON'T CALL HIM OVER HERE... HE SCARES ME.

B **00**

HEY, LOOK WHO'S JOINING THE BALLET CLASS.

A

I DON'T CARE WHAT YOU SAY ABOUT YOGA. I THINK YOU LOOK SILLY STANDING ON YOUR HEAD.
P
d

Y'KNOW, QUINCY... GETTING TOGETHER WAS THE SMARTEST THING WE EVER DID.
IQ

HEY, LOOK AT HER! SHE'S HAD A NOSE JOB.
WHY DO YOU HAVE TO EXPLAIN EVERYTHING?

LOOK, CHARLEY,,
NOBODY LIKES
A BIG MOUTH!

CC

LET'S FACE
IT, FELLAS,
LIFE IS
FULL OF
LITTLE
SURPRISES,

ESP

I THINK
THOSE
BACKLESS
DRESSES
ARE VULGAR

BB   **3**

LISTEN... BETTER LATE THAN NEVER.
AM PM

YOU CAN'T FOOL ME, HARRY... I'VE GOT YOUR NUMBER.
H#

IF HE COMES OVER HERE I'LL SCREAM!
EE K

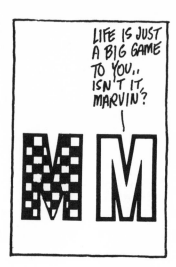

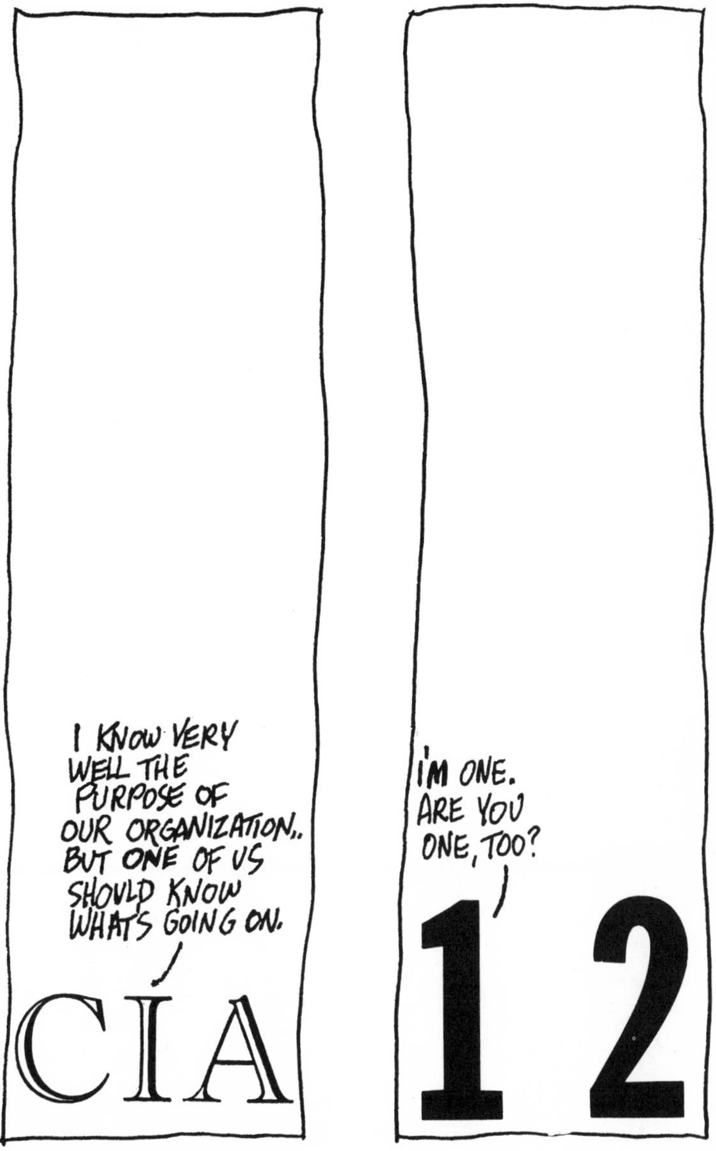
I KNOW VERY WELL THE PURPOSE OF OUR ORGANIZATION.. BUT ONE OF US SHOULD KNOW WHATS GOING ON.
CIA
I'M ONE. ARE YOU ONE, TOO?
1 2

IT'S BAD LUCK EVERY TIME WE GET TOGETHER.
1 3

WHAT MAKES YOU THINK YOU'RE SO HOT?
32° 90°

THERE'S NOTHING TO IT IF YOU TIGHTEN YOUR BELT.
hhk

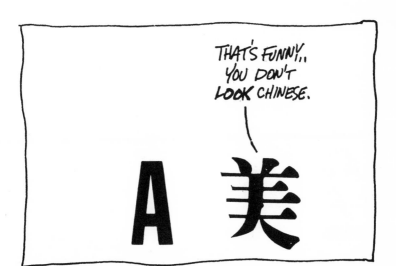

FOR HEAVEN'S SAKE, ARNOLD, KEEP A CIVIL TONGUE IN YOUR HEAD!
A A
I DON'T CARE WHAT THEY SAY... I SAY THE WORLD IS FLAT.
1492
AS FAR AS I'M CONCERNED, ORVILLE, YOU'RE JUST A BIG NOTHING!
0 0

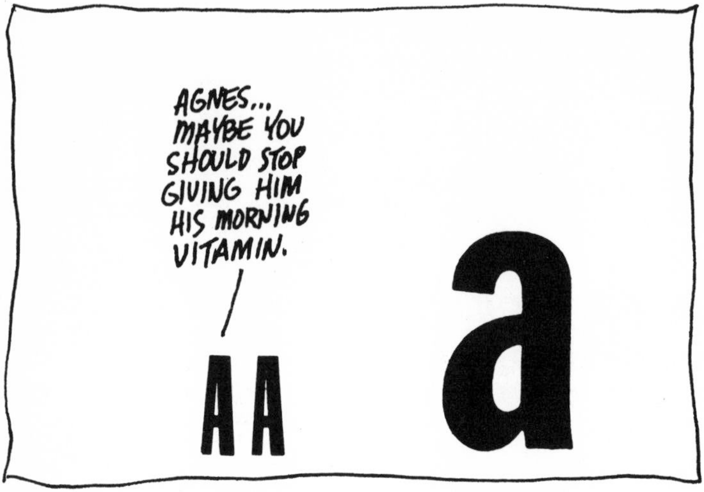
AGNES... MAYBE YOU SHOULD STOP GIVING HIM HIS MORNING VITAMIN.
AA
a

THERE'S NOTHING TO IT, FREDDIE. JUST STAND UP STRAIGHT AND HOLD IN YOUR STOMACH!
U
V

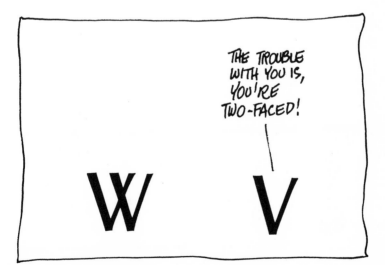

EITHER YOU GO ON A DIET ORVIL, OR WE'RE GETTING TWIN BEDS.

O o

WHO WOULD HAVE THOUGHT IT... OUR SON, A BALLET DANCER.

YY *Y*

PARDON ME.. IS THIS THE BAR CAR?
FORGET IT. YOU HAVEN'T GOT A LEG TO STAND ON
SO I SAID, "CUT IT OUT HENRY"... AND HE DID.

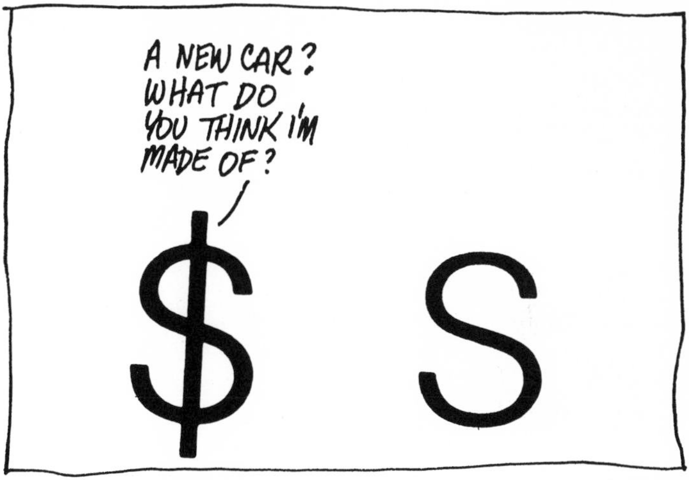
A NEW CAR? WHAT DO YOU THINK I'M MADE OF?
$ S

THE TROUBLE WITH YOU IS.. YOU HAVE NO BACKBONE.
Z 2

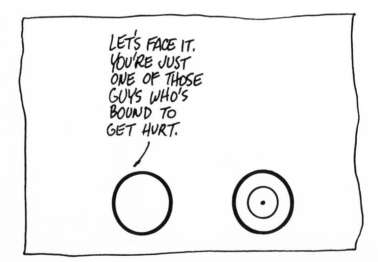

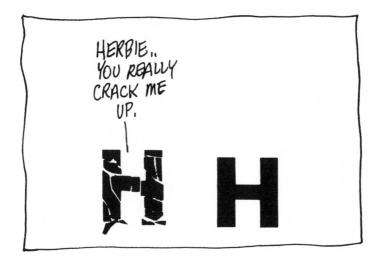

FOR GOODNESS
SAKE .. PULL
YOURSELF
TOGETHER !

AA

I WAS
GETTING ON
THE BUS..
AND JUST
LIKE THAT..
THE DOORS
CLOSED ON
ME.

HH

WHY ARE
YOU ALWAYS
CAPITALIZING
ON ME ?

Ee

REPENT! THE END IS NEAR
WXY

IF WE LET HIM IN I JUST KNOW WE'RE FINISHED.
e nd

AS FAR
AS I'M
CONCERNED,
ZELDA...
YOU'RE
THE END.

AZ